100

The Other Face

Experiencing the Mask

Edited by
Wendy Klein and Brent Robison

Bliss Plot
P R E S S

Dear Carolyn,
For the
many masks
you share with
me. :. Wendy

The Other Face
Experiencing the Mask

Edited by Wendy Klein and Brent Robison

Copyright © 2003, Bliss Plot Press

Published by Bliss Plot Press, PO Box 68, Mt. Tremper, NY 12457
www.blissplotpress.com

Wendy Klein Masks
www.wendyklein.com

ISBN 0-9718908-3-8
Library of Congress Control Number: 2003097660

Printed in the United States of America
1st Edition

Cover design by Wendy Klein and Brent Robison
Cover art by Flint Butera (artphobia.com)
Other images © 2003 Clipart.com

Copyrights and Acknowledgments

Quotations:

"The Critic as Artist, Part 2" by Oscar Wilde, *Intentions* (1891)

"Everything and Nothing" by Jorge Luis Borges, translated by James E. Irby, *Labyrinths* © 1964 New Directions Publishing Company

"Archetypes of the Collective Unconscious" (1935) and "Psychological Aspects of the Kore" (1941), by Carl Gustav Jung, *Collected Works of C.G. Jung, Volume 9, Part I: The Archetypes and the Collective Unconscious*, edited and translated by Gerhard Adler and R.F.C. Hull, © Princeton University Press

"My New Book," *The Poet Game* by Greg Brown, Red House Records, lyrics © 1994 Brown-Feldman Publishing

"Sexual Personae: The Cancelled Preface," *Sex, Art, and American Culture* © 1992, Camille Paglia, Vintage Books

"How I Became a Madman," *The Madman: His Parables and Poems* (1918), Kahlil Gibran

"The Fox and the Mask, " *Aesop's Fables*, translated byGeorge Fyler Townsend (1814-1900)

"What is Noble: 289," *Beyond Good & Evil* by Friedrich Nietzsche, translated by Walter Kaufmann, © 1966, Random House, Inc.

Man is least himself when he talks in his own person. Give him a mask, and he will tell you the truth.

—Oscar Wilde

Contents

The Other Face
Experiencing the Mask

Introduction in Two Parts

For more than a decade now I've been asked many questions about the general concept of masks. The reason for this is that I create handcrafted masks for a living. In the process of showing and selling my work I'm thought to be a so-called "expert" on the subject. This is far from true. In many ways, I've been confounded by my chosen path and have found myself at a loss to enlighten those who ask me about the meaning of what I do. *It's a very mysterious thing* has been written across the door of my limited understanding, and so something equally obscure has been my usual response. Thankfully, the setting in which I've been asked these questions has left little room for what I would consider a more thoughtful answer. I wasn't ready.

For me, this compilation of writings has brought with it a kind of revelation. It's not only as an editor that I read each word carefully and more than once. It's as an artist that I let myself absorb these passages. The connection between my self and the livelihood I was so wordlessly drawn to years ago has come full circle. In this sense, there is little separation between what I do and what I am—a maskmaker. In addition to that, there is support in these writings for a thought I've carried with me over the years. It's that every mask is an encrypted confession of sorts and that each confession is a dare for us to look deeper and beyond the surface in search of its meaning.

These writing focus on the psychological and spiritual aspects of the masks we wear and are meant to broaden understanding of ourselves and to express a truth of individual being. However lofty this may sound, I believe there is a deeper understanding to be gained by reading on. My hope is that you'll do so with an eye toward allowing exploration of your inner masks. They are many.

I hope you will enjoy this book.

Wendy Hein

I am wearing a mask. Right now, as I write this. It is not a physical thing covering my face; rather, it is in the "I" that begins this paragraph. Again, now: I write "I" followed by a verb, and you the reader perceive me, a writer, telling you his own "truth." But no matter what I write, "I" is a lie. And no matter what I write, "I" is also the truth.

If I were writing here in a mode called "fiction," you would gladly accept the mask and maybe even think, "how creative." There are three works of fiction in this book: When R.L. Stevenson wears the face of his invention Dr. Jekyll and says, "I was born in the year 18— to a large fortune...," we enter into a kind of theater and suspend our disbelief. Our pleasure is in believing the obvious lie. When Barry Yourgrau starts, "I come into the kitchen," we're not so sure that this is an invented persona speaking, but we go along happily as his darkish whimsy unfolds. Mark Sherman's "I" may make us squirm a bit because, while his story has the trappings of fiction, the narrator, we think, just might be Mr. Sherman himself, pretending otherwise. The mask grows thinner.

2

But there are "non-fiction" works in this volume as well. Like this introduction: since it is not fiction, it must be true, right? The mask of "I" is not acknowledged; it is a sly disguise that looks similar enough to my real face (is there such a thing?) that you don't suspect I wear a mask at all. Michael Perkins, Sparrow, and Gabriel Q all write an "I" that also makes no suggestion of a mask. Does that mean their works are "true?"

Samuel Avital, Sophie Rogers-Gessert, Vincent Lloyd, and George Ulrich don't need an "I" at all; they wear the masks of authority, of objectivity, of educated reason. But simply to set pen to paper, one must adopt the persona of "writer." Carl Jung said, "The persona is a complicated system of relations between individual consciousness and society, fittingly enough a kind of mask, designed on the one hand to make a definite impression upon others, and, on the other, to conceal the true nature of the individual."

I write fiction. I believe in the power of imagination, and I have often "hired" someone not myself—a persona—to narrate my stories. Oscar Wilde was right: behind that mask, my conscious agendas, my censors, my carefully constructed "self," all disappear, and without "me" in control, I tell the truth. The real truth. It slips in through the unguarded back door. It can't be otherwise, because I am I.

Except, of course, for the Buddhist truth that "I" is just an illusion anyway. As Alan Watts said, "I" is just the Universe "eyeing." Each of us is both the center and not the center: double in nature. Dr. Jekyll can't face himself as he writes about Hyde: "He, I say—I cannot say, I." He denies his own double nature even as he admits it. In a similar self-deconstruction, H.G. Wells' *Invisible Man* turns his unhappy being into apparent nothingness and then, hiding in a costumier's shop, must put on a mask and false whiskers to make himself again perceptible in the world. The masked man always dons another mask, and so it goes.

Pablo Picasso said: "Art is a lie that tells the truth." This book, our little work of art, is full of masks, but it is also full of

truth. I hope you'll read it with an open heart, and receive wisd
And as for whether these warm wishes come from "me" or f
some persona in my employ, I feel as Jorge Luis Borges d
when he closes the story "Borges and I"...

I do not know which of us has written this page.

"I who have been so many men in vain want to be one and myself." The voice of the Lord answered from a whirlwind: "Neither am I anyone; I have dreamt the world as you dreamt your work, my Shakespeare, and among the forms in my dream are you, who like myself are many and no one."

—Jorge Luis Borges
Everything and Nothing

Whoever looks into the mirror of the water will see first of all his own face. Whoever goes to himself risks a confrontation with himself. The mirror does not flatter, it faithfully shows whatever looks into it; namely, the face we never show to the world because we cover it with the persona, the mask of the actor. But the mirror lies behind the mask and shows the true face.

—Carl Jung
Archetypes of the Collective Unconscious

Original Face

Michael Perkins

"What was your original face, before you were born?"
— Zen teaching

Cleaning the mirror by moonlight,
I uncover the first of my faces,
Hidden from myself all these
Dissembled years. The portrait
Is out of focus at first,
Still new; but I can see that
It is unsympathetically true.
As I watch, it gathers the many
Into the unknown One —
And it is too late to wish
I had not begun.

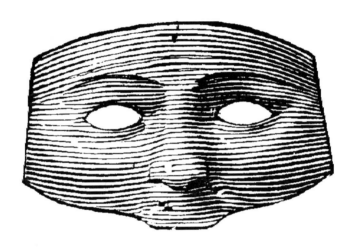

8

Facing the Mask

Samuel Avital

Sit with the spine straight, in stillness. Hold the mask in your hands and look at it. Observe the texture and other details. It's part of your skin that you have peeled. It's a replica of your physical face. Think no thoughts other than about the mask. Look at the shape of the features. Do not judge, just look. Look at the eyes. They appear as two holes that reach infinity. Become familiar with your face that you hold in your hands.

This tool, the mask, is a place. It's not a time. Become friends with the mask and it will teach you many things. Your face is looking at you. It is covered, somehow, by different thoughts.

Very slowly put the mask on your face. Take five million years to do this. No brusque movements. Every movement should be very conscious. With the mask on, keep the eyes closed. Breathe very calmly. Begin to feel your own facial structure under the mask. It is covered, as if by clothes.

Visualize yourself sitting in water up to your neck. It is the ocean. What you see is the horizon of the waters. Nourish the waters, the horizon, and ask who is behind the mask. It has no name. Is it your face? Is the mask really that important, or is it just a tool to help us realize the essence? No attributes, no name, no concept—totally pure. If we can grasp that ungraspable, then later we can express that essence.

Find the neutral one, the no-name one, the circle, the empty one within. That center of the circle is there living behind every being.

Open the eyes halfway. What you see on the other side of the horizon is the reflection of yourself. Be detached from it. There is no such thing as near or far. You cannot measure the horizon. The water is cool and helps the body in that total peace.

In very slow motion, like moving for the first time, check to see if the mask is still there. The hands don't touch as if they know, they touch as if they want to know. Look at your hands through the windows of your eyes.

Stand up using very slow motion. Who is behind the mask moving the body? It is a new physical being that you discover, but who is discovering it? Who is moving the body from the inside? The goal is to stand. Do not plan any movement. Let the one behind the mask move you.

Once you stand, get in touch with that presence. The presence is not you. It's no-name. If we are aware of it, everything becomes fresh, as if for the first time. Let the presence walk, using the vehicle of the body. Any movement we do now is in the service of walking, with appreciation and reverence. The presence goes for a promenade. It is not limited in any way. Turn. When the head meets the limitation of the body, the presence continues. The presence will teach you to turn.

Now we take certain conditions and see how the presence relates. Be cold! Let coldness contract the body, as the presence stays remote, observing the expression of the body. Watch how the mask keeps the face from interfering in the body's expression. Now change; be hot! Immediately the body expands and droops, but the presence stays distant.

The body takes on archetypes. Be a warrior! The archetype of the warrior is one who knows his power and knows how to use it positively. Be a coward! Receive the universal coward in you. Cowardice is not negative; it is a state of being. Let the presence teach you how to use the body as a brush. Presence never needs to justify itself. The presence knows.

Come back to the original spot where you began. The presence sits like a king or queen. It knows how to sit. The one who is sitting has a right to be there. Turn the head to brush the horizon. Just the head. *C'est une noblesse de presence.* Close the windows and sit still in the waters. Very slowly, eyes closed, take off the mask and hold it facing you.

The Mask

Mark Sherman

"So, how are you doing today?" he asked.

"I'm fine," I replied.

He was silent. Why the fuck am I here? I said to myself. I know why *he's* here. He's getting two dollars a minute. Even when he says nothing. He's making money just sitting there.

"What do you want me to say?" I asked.

Still silence.

The motherfucker.

I don't want to say anything. My life is going okay. Why do I have to talk about everything?

"Go ahead," he said. "Whatever comes to mind."

I couldn't stand it any more. My brother said it was okay to express anger at your therapist, that he did it all the time. What was I afraid of?

"Whatever comes to mind?!" I said. "Whatever comes to mind? Well, here's what comes to mind. What the fuck am I doing here?! I was doing fine in my life. I was writing and singing and being alive. I was even happy sometimes. And now I come here every week, for what? For your silence, your staring at me? I have the same problems I had when I came in. And you're a lot richer. I hate this."

"So why do you keep coming?" he asked. "No one's forcing you. You could leave right now if you wanted to. Go ahead. Leave."

"Sure," I said. "And get charged for the whole session. What a racket. Shit, what a racket."

13

"No," he said. "No charge for today, if you leave now. I'm not saying I want you to, but you can. With no charge."

"Sure," I said. "And then I can't come back, right? Like my dad with his patients. 'Get yourself another doctor,' he'd scream at them. He didn't need them. They needed him."

"You could come back next week," he said. "I'm not your dad. Your dad is dead."

I could feel the tears starting to come.

"You want me to cry, don't you?" I said. "That's what you want. That's the therapist's orgasm, isn't it? Shit," I said, feeling my eyes moisten.

"Go ahead," he said. "Don't be afraid of it. Let it out."

"Why?" I said, practically sobbing now. "Why? It doesn't help. I want to get somewhere in my life, not keep thinking about my father."

There was silence again.

I took a tissue from the table and blew my nose and dried my eyes.

"So let's talk about your dad a little," he said.

"Why? He fucked me up. Yeah, he had his problems, but he was a father. I'm a father. I'm not destroying my kids."

Silence.

"What? Are you saying I'm not a good father? That too? The one area I thought I was okay?"

"I didn't say anything," he said.

"I don't hit my kids," I said. "And I don't humiliate them. And I tell them all the time that I love them. What the fuck am I supposed to do?"

"What about *your* father?" he said. "Did he ever tell you he loved you?"

"Are you kidding?" I said. "Not that I can remember. My mom barely ever said it either. But he must have loved me. I saw letters he wrote to my mom when he was overseas. He kept asking about me, and saying how much he missed me. He called me his little sweetie-boy. He must have loved me. He must have. He did, didn't he?"

Silence.

"Say something. I can't stand this silence stuff. That's what he used to do when he was really angry at me. He'd just stop talking to me. He'd tell my mother what he wanted to say to me, and she'd say it. She'd say it! She'd say it! Why didn't she just say 'You tell him. Don't ask me to do this.'? What was she afraid of?"

"What do you think?" he asked.

"She was afraid of him, wasn't she?" I said. "We were all afraid of him. Fuck him. How could he do that? What was wrong with him? Why was he so angry all the time?"

"Angry all the time?" he said. "Who does that remind you of?"

The "other" in us always seems alien and unacceptable; but if we let ourselves be aggrieved the feeling sinks in, and we are the richer for this little bit of self-knowledge.

—Carl Jung
Psychological Aspects of the Kore

A Scholarly Exchange

A Humanist Critique of the Mask
Sophie Rogers–Gessert

Revaluation of the Mask
Vincent Lloyd

A Humanist Critique of the Mask

Sophie Rogers-Gessert

The word "person" originated in and was borrowed from theater. *Persona* was the Latin word for the large identifying masks that early Greek actors wore to portray the roles of their characters. Because of the size of the amphitheaters where they performed, subtlety was an ineffectual visual technique. The masks made certain characteristic traits easily recognizable to the audience. Nuance was exchanged for clarity and common comprehension.

Today, the words "mask" and "persona" both connote an aspect of oneself which is presented to the world for its approval. Both "mask" and "persona" negotiate the place between public and private selves where who we are collides with who we think we should appear to be. Our perceptions of these words are tainted by their association with artificiality and falsity—the deliberate misrepresentation of oneself, one's emotions, and one's thoughts.

As actors on life's stage, we are capable of creating illusory characters for ourselves, exaggerating some emotions while shrouding others, scripting conversations and interactions, and denying ourselves communication of certain ideas. In these ways we edit ourselves in an attempt to convince the world that we are likable.

Habitual falsity effects a cognitive imbalance of illusion of one's perception of oneself. We come to believe in our surface assertions and thereby deny to ourselves knowledge of our own intentions and motivations. The danger is in allowing the facade to transform one's inner self. In metaphors, words point to and stand in for other words. In language in general, words point to and stand in for facts and real things. Substitution is an action, one which entails profound, albeit unrecognized, responsibility.

When we speak, we choose between innumerable possible topics, thought constructions, word combinations, tones of voice. We choose not only which thoughts to communicate and how we will communicate them, but to whom: with this last choice, we become accountable for not only our own expression, but also partially for the listener's response to what they hear and see.

One function of the mask is to censor what we communicate to others, whether verbally or non-verbally. Our masks, with varying degrees of efficacy, control how we are perceived—which aspects are veiled while others become prominent. The mask's purpose is not necessarily to hide the individual but to allow a particular aspect of the individual to be communicated with greater focus and intensity.

The mask can also function as a lubricant to ease social friction and avoid conflicts, by censoring potentially offensive or threatening statements. The downside of this ability is that our societally-prescribed preoccupation with courtesy can allow too much to be left unsaid. The conflicts our masks allow us to evade may be the very interactions which would be the most challenging to our ideas and possibly the most enlightening. Conflicts catalyze the search for truth. Through conflicts, we can identify false beliefs and contest assumptions.

Other people's perspectives can transform and elucidate our own ideas. The power of intelligence is more fully realized through interaction and exchange; realization is a reaction. Humanism teaches us that designation of an object, concept, or text as sacred becomes problematic since it is considered disrespectful to question it. Questioning is the very thing which keeps ideas alive; they are perpetuated through reexamination and transmission. As they pass from person to person, they are subtly transformed and thus they evolve. To disallow questioning of an idea or ideology is to preempt the process of adaptation to our ever-changing world, and consequently ensure its eventual extinction.

Humanist philosophy thus opens doors which were too long locked shut because of the supposition that inquiry was blasphemous. Philosophy teaches us that reason, not faith, is the path to truth. Self-examination and methodological inquiry are the philosophic engagements; asking is our answer. Yet our questions and our appreciation of the process of inquiry depend upon our preexisting assumptions about value, goodness, truth. C.S. Lewis writes, "What we learn from experience depends on the kind of philosophy we bring to experience" (*Miracles: a Preliminary Study*). How can we move beyond the confines of our individual expectations and assumptions in order to mobilize reason's objective powers?

A key to learning is to actively seek departures from familiar thought. All forms of perception, including intellectual perception, depend upon a series of choices. What do you choose to look at? What do you choose to pay attention to? And indeed, especially in today's society, attention is a thing which is paid. We all possess the means by which to define our conception of ourselves, our society, our world. If we, as humanists, are to commit ourselves to the pursuit of learning in place of dogma, tolerance instead of paranoia, compassion over sheer selfishness, and deliberative reason rather than blind faith, we must acknowledge that dynamic, honest, and open inter- and intra-communicative process is indispensable.

Ideas, whether good or bad, are animated through communication. Without communication our rational and emotional faculties wither. The mask hinders the honest and complete transmission of ideas. We frame our thoughts according to conventions of language, expression, and courtesy. We edit them to avoid conflict. We also possess the ability to create false identities which threaten our own internal authenticity. The issue here is not disclosure.

As we know, honesty doesn't require revealing all of our private selves. In fact, much of what defines us as individuals is the choice of which aspects we wish to reveal. Rather, our concern with the mask as humanists is the degree of investment and involvement to which our social roles allow us to engage in interaction. In seeking egress from the confines of familiar thinking, we must strive to be responsive on a number of levels, to take full advantage of opportunities to exchange thought, and to build upon the structures of prudential reason which sustain the common ground of solitary communication.

A commitment to humanism and the free exchange of thoughts entails seeking to divest ourselves of the apparent social advantages of dissimulation and instead strive toward congruence between expression and actual feeling. If we insist upon truth in thought, we must also be committed to pursuing truthful interaction. As Hawthorne once wrote, "Be true! Be true! Be true! Show freely to the world, if not your worst, yet some trait by which the worst may be inferred" (*The Scarlet Letter*). To reveal what one is ashamed of may seem a risky or foolish aim. However, identifying and examining our sources of shame and guilt is imperative to the complete questioning of our assumptions and our society.

Anxiety of expression reveals our devaluation of particular traits and ideas. Articulation of what we fear, hate, or disapprove of about ourselves is a difficult and painful venture. But those who attempt it may be rewarded by realizing their shame was needless and by gaining awareness of their actual weaknesses. Both of these experiences aid us in our pursuit of truth and self-knowledge.

Many of the issues of the mask are alluded to in Castiglione's *The Book of the Courtier*, in which a group of 16th century nobility exchange conceptions of the ideal courtier, the perfect man. They discuss everything from the appropriate style of dress and movement to the morality of obeying orders. In one section, they discuss the "correct" attitude towards dance, specifying that the courtier should "maintain a certain dignity, though tempered by the lightness and delicate grace of his movements." He should restrain himself from attempting "those quick movements of the feet and double steps...unless he is at a masked ball...".

The ramifications of these instructions extend beyond the realm of the dance floor. Throughout *The Book of the Courtier* itself, the speakers dance lightly across their topics of discussion, careful not to delve too deeply, speak too seriously, or "attempt those quick movements of the feet" or quick movements of reason and logic. Like the dancers, the ideal courtier is said to be primarily concerned with making a positive impression on those who are listening and watching.

The dance is not a dance in its own right—it is a stage, and the movements played out on this stage are designed for a certain response. The courtier is expected to use flattery, bravery, virtue, and modesty to his best advantage. He is not expected to be truly admiring, truly brave, truly virtuous, much less truly modest. Each action must be tailored to the expectations of the onlookers. Everything which is spoken or expressed in the presence of others is not merely a statement or expression, but a message. The courtier's hidden agenda in all interactions must concern the possible gains and advantages of acting in certain ways, saying certain things. Do the ends of interaction justify the means? Whether or not one's means concurs with the meaning of what he says and does, as long as the acting is competent and the mask does not slip, his actions will have the same effect. So why, the social-dancers may ask, should only those who are naturally blessed with positive traits benefit from them? Why not just simulate those desirable traits while keeping one's personal goals in mind?

Politically and socially speaking, the masked deception of the ideal courtier is certainly an effective method to obtain success. Honest expression of ideas and emotions is usually not conducive to achieving ambitious goals. It is conducive, however, to obtaining a degree of engagement with one's own thoughts and with other people, an engagement which cannot possibly be reached through falsity. Falsity, in its most polished form, is a dancer who makes no missteps and who charms all who watch. Honesty, however, is a dancer who dances for the sake of doing justice to the music—and through the music, doing herself justice.

Revaluation of the Mask

Vincent Lloyd

Both in popular culture and in intellectual debate one often hears that an individual must work to "unmask" himself or herself in order to facilitate the free exchange of ideas as well as to promote truthful interactions. Only through "unmasked" interactions does true freethought take place: as Sophie Rogers-Gessert put it, "The mask hinders the honest and complete transmission of ideas.... A commitment to humanism entails seeking to divest ourselves of the apparent social advantages of dissimulation and instead strive toward congruence between expression and actual feeling."

We will explore this notion of the "mask" being a hindrance to "honest" communication by contextualizing and historicizing the discussion, then looking at a masked protagonist from proto-Existentialist literature, and finally demonstrating the utter incoherence of the concept of the "mask", thereby making moot the supposed obligation for the humanist to take off his or her own mask.

First, the concept of the "mask" necessarily implies a conception of authenticity. To be masked implies that something is being covered and stays unrevealed—something thought of as the "authentic" self—and that authenticity is synonymous with "unmasked interactions." Only a few aspects of this vast subject (a subject with implications to the concept of self, personality and responsibility) will be explored here.

Literary criticLionel Trilling put forth the notion that there have been two related notions of personal truthfulness: sincerity and authenticity. In pre-modern times, the dominant notion was sincerity—individuals were to be truthful in their interactions with others. For example, if you were asked whether you had a spare bedroom by a traveler, you were to tell the truth. The prevalence of this view, Trilling argues, is seen in the literature of the time, where duplicity was parodied and mocked, and the scoundrel was the double-dealer.

With the advent of modernity, the growth of the state, the increasing complexity of individual roles, the increasing emphasis on the role of the individual, and related phenomena, the concept of sincerity became obsolescent. Individuals had to deal with multiple audiences and the sincere individual began being portrayed as simple-minded and naive. Instead of sincerity, a new notion of authenticity emerged in culture and literature; one where, instead of being absolutely truthful in all interactions with others, the new ideal was to be truthful with one's self. The new protagonist was wrestling to reconcile his outward actions with his inward feelings.

That the shift from sincerity to authenticity coincided with the dawn of the modern era is no coincidence: modernity imposed increasing numbers of constraints on individuals and imposed a need for greater number of interactions—both causing increasing dissonance between "authentic" feeling and actual action. Moreover, social (non-democratic) and intellectual (e.g. Kant and Hegel) hierarchies and orders were being overturned, leaving uncertainty about the moral value of absolute sincerity and creating an opening for emphasis on the subjective and individual experience.

The great early example of this is the praise of the natural, unencumbered man in Rousseau's writings. Such a view has only increased in the years since Rousseau. Today we have seen what one theorist calls the "commercialization" of emotions: flight attendants, for example, are encouraged to bring their natural energy and happiness to work and utilize it in customer interactions. On September 11, the media led the country in a collective emotional experience of mourning. The more emotions are externally controlled, the more individuals and society value the spontaneous and uncontrolled. In order to harness this, an entire industry has sprung up catering to individuals wishing to be reconnected with their "true selves:" from psychotherapists to practitioners of Eastern religions.

The problem we are concerned with then is that of one's reconciliation of the "true self" with one's actions, as opposed to the question of sincerity's value in complex interpersonal interactions. This problem is not omnipresent in human history but is a symptom of modernity and specifically the societal-individual interactions that are the products of modernity.

The Canadian philosopher Charles Taylor examines the consequences of the modern emphasis on authenticity. He believes that the emphasis on connecting individual emotion with action necessarily leads to relativism: each individual is seeking self-fulfillment to express their own feelings and desires. This leads to a politics of liberal neutrality in which society ought to take no moral positions lest it create dissonance between the (suggested or required) actions of individuals and their "true" emotions and understandings. This can lead to the destructive consequence of societal fragmentation and compartmentalization.

Both the existentialist perspective on authenticity and the more recent structuralist and post-structuralist thought on the subject grow out of the intellectual seeds sowed by Nietzsche. In the second of his Untimely Meditations, Nietzsche asserts the existence of a disconnect between the true man and the actual man constrained by society and the State. If man allows for this latter self to dominate with no interest in the former, he lets his existence be "a thoughtless accident." But Nietzsche's analysis is in some ways subtler than his existentialist successors for he acknowledges the paradox inherent in this quest for reconciliation: "What does your conscience say? 'You shall become who you are'" (*The Gay Science*).

Simone de Beauvoir, following in the existentialist tradition popularized by Sartre, considers the "serious man"—her formulation of a similar character developed by Nietzsche—in *The Ethics of Ambiguity*. The serious man is a dishonest man, an inauthentic man, a man who denies his freedom because he "chooses to live in an infantile world" out of fear or lack of confidence. The serious man submits his freedom to external authority: he is the Christian, the Communist, the unquestioning. He abandons his true self, living forever masked.

De Beauvoir admits that there are constraints on this freedom (for example enslavement), but it is the task of the free man to exercise his freedom: "a man who has the necessary instruments to escape this lie and who does not want to use them consumes his freedom in denying them. He makes himself serious." Out of this notion of freedom to express the true self comes the imperative to women to loose the bonds that constrain them, the masks that they wear: although "women inherit a long tradition of submission ... there is often laziness and timidity in their resignation; their honesty is not quite complete; but to the extent that it exists, their freedom remains available, it is not denied."

Explorations of authenticity from the French intellectual tradition of the second half of the 20th century end in paradox: after deconstructing the self and the notion of the authentic, all that is left for the individual is to engage in a sort of "aesthetics of the self"—to create one's life as a work of art.

French philosopher Michel Foucault, starting from an explicit rejection of the existentialist project (the rejection of which was so central to his work), arrives at a startlingly similar conclusion: "From the idea that the self is not given to us, I think that there is only one practical consequence: we have to create ourselves as a work of art" (*On the Genealogy of Ethics*). The only difference seems to be that whereas the existentialists argue that the self is handed to each individual on a platter and it is our task to remove the barriers between us and the food and partake in it, Foucault and others are making the argument that we are given neither food nor a platter, but must imagine it, conjure it up, it being amorphous, not necessarily in the form of food or even a platter.

In 1892, a full half-century before the appearance of Albert Camus' novel *The Stranger*, the Norwegian author Knut Hamsun published *Mysteries*. Hamsun (who won the Nobel Prize in literature in 1920) is generally classified with existentialist writers, despite his significantly earlier chronology. The protagonist of *Mysteries*, Johan Nagel, arrives in a small Norwegian town. It is not clear where he came from, where he is going, or why he is there. Nagel moves into the town's hotel, saying few words to the puzzled local residents.

Nagel eventually begins to interact with the community: he defends an imbecile who is being taken advantage of by a town official. Why does he do this? It is not clear.

Nagel has with his luggage a violin case, but in it there is no violin. He volunteers to an interlocutor that he carries this case simply to make a good impression on people, to make them think that he is learned, that he is the sort of person that would play a violin. But then, at the town fair, Nagel happens to borrow someone's violin and plays beautifully.

Shortly after his arrival, Nagel takes a long walk outside of town for a day. When he returns, a telegram is awaiting him concerning the sale of some property of his. Again, later in the book he volunteers that he had in fact sent this telegram to himself (from the neighboring town to which he walked) so as to appear to be a man of wealth. But are we to trust him? This continues throughout the book: whatever information Nagel gives, he gives it self-consciously, and depending on his audience the information differs.

So we should say that, using Trilling's analysis of sincerity and authenticity, Nagel is a completely insincere character—a modern character—for he has to perform for multiple audiences. But how authentic is he? This is a question which Hamsun does not allow the reader to answer for everything we know about Nagel is filtered through the perspective of Nagel—we see him only masked, albeit not always with the same mask on, and from this we can conclude nothing about what lies behind the masks. Unlike *The Stranger* in which we also are given a minimalist picture of the protagonist, Camus' protagonist is "unmasked," showing his "true self," whereas Hamsun's Nagel is perpetually masked.

If we knew more about Nagel, could we discover what was behind his masks, his "true self"? The answer is clearly no; we can increase the number of interactions in which we observe him to be participating, but in each interaction he simply wears a different mask. Do the townspeople with whom he interacts only express their "true selves"? They are certainly more stable in their personalities, but this doesn't mean they are more "genuine", they simply wear just one mask. As sociologist Robert Park wrote:

"It is probably no mere historical accident that the word 'person', in its first meaning, is a mask. It is rather a recognition of the fact that everyone is always and everywhere, more or less consciously, playing a role... It is in these roles that we know each other; it is in these roles that we know ourselves" (*Race and Culture*).

The question of the "authenticity" of Nagel is unanswerable because of the incoherence of the dualistic notion of "true self" versus "masked self." Even Camus' protagonist is part of a tradition, shaped by externalities (a poor term since it implies a clear distinction between the "external" and "internal"). Psychologists attempt to dissent—the true self, they argue, the unencumbered ego, may very well be shaped by external factors —for example, biological and cultural ones—but it is distinguishable, it develops in childhood and adolescence as part of personal identity formation. But why can we consider it static? Why isolate a point in time and say any changes after this are "unnatural," counter to the "true self"? Is this not like saying that the US Constitution, as it was interpreted up to, say, 1900, was a dynamic document, but since then it became static?

Let us revisit some of the discussions of authenticity encountered earlier. Recall that Taylor argued that support for the "quest for authenticity" leads to relativism and a fragmented, amoral society of liberal neutrality. But we can now see that Taylor errs in his assignment of causality. It is not necessarily the case that the quest for authenticity leads to an amoral society, but rather that a society and historical tradition shape each individual's quest for authenticity, since the masks that are omnipresent on our faces are mass-produced, and only the most minute details differ.

Recall also that de Beauvoir argued that it was the task of man and woman in particular to exercise freedom in not allowing masks to be placed on one's self, to remove masks already in place, and to exercise the existential individual freedom behind them. But the search for this existential freedom, as we have seen, is a futile quest: the creation of a unique space for the "true self" is impossible.

The preeminent woman's historian Carroll Smith-Rosenberg has analyzed the historical problems of women's roles from a perspective heavily influenced by post-structuralist thought. Her classic essay "The Female World of Love and Ritual" considers the intimate female-female relationships that developed in Victorian America. She concludes that these relationships developed because of the structural factors present at the time. Specifically, with a rigid demarcation between men's spheres and roles and women's spheres and roles, such relationships were a coping mechanism providing necessary emotional and physical intimacy (analogous to homosexuality in modern prisons, she points out). This is the sort of productive analysis that is important: instead of searching for the way in which each of these Victorian women threw off culturally imposed "masks" and expressed an inner existential freedom (as de Beauvoir might have reasoned), Smith-Rosenberg realizes, like Park, that all inter- and intra-personal displays are masks created by "external" forces, and it is in the complex navigation of these masks—not quite a stripping away; perhaps an unfolding—that what has been called the "quest for authenticity" occurs.

30

Two Poems

Sparrow

Fluxus Poem No. 6

Cut a hole in this page.

Whatever you see through the page will be the poem.

Anti-Mask

I dissolve
masks!
I rip them up!

Unbind all faces,
everywhere!

One day, long before many gods were born, I woke from a deep sleep and all my masks were stolen, the seven masks I have fashioned and worn in seven lives. I ran maskless through the crowded streets shouting, "Thieves, thieves, the cursed thieves."

And when I reached the market place, a youth standing on a housetop cried, "He is a madman." I looked up to behold him; the sun kissed my own naked face for the first time. For the first time the sun kissed my own naked face and my soul was inflamed with love for the sun, and I wanted my masks no more. And as if in a trance I cried, "Blessed, blessed are the thieves who stole my masks."

Thus I became a madman.

—Kahlil Gibran
The Madman

Coyote sleeps with everyone,
but in the morning he's long gone
and it turns out that he was a she.
Tales grow tall around the fire.
Where there's no truth, no one's a liar.
Whatever mask you wear is who you'll be.

—Greg Brown
"My New Book"
The Poet Game

Masks: a History

George Ulrich

As humans we base our identities on our bodies. Of all the parts of the body, it is the face that is most closely associated with the individual "self." Age and sex are obvious identifications, as are other natural, biological features such as "taking after Dad." But social identity and status (married/single, sacred/secular, chief/commoner) are symbolic and require alteration of the body or face in order to communicate or change identity. This is done by either taking something away such as teeth or hair, or adding something through ornamentation: cosmetics, costumes, or masks, or various combinations of these.

A mask is any device which wholly or partially conceals the face. It is significant to note the word "person" derives from a Greek word meaning mask, or the role played by an actor in a dramatic performance. Thus our faces reveal our social selves: who we are in relation to other members of our society by virtue of the roles we play in it. Persona, "the mask," is related to personality, the self or ego we reveal to the world. Masks have the ability to conceal, change, or transform the "person" behind the image into something or someone else. This metaphoric "else," this "as if" quality of masks makes them both playful and powerful, and relates them to ritual, religion, and myth. Masks allow us to pretend, and much more.

As a case in point, have you ever watched children on Halloween? When a child puts on a vampire costume, you can bet that sometime, somewhere, someone's going to get bitten. For a

35

brief period of time a five-year-old has taken on the power and persona of a legendary Transylvanian Count. Masks transform adults in a similar way. I have seen fully grown women cackle all night behind a witch's image, and mature men in red tights behave "devilishly" while horned, tailed and goateed. In "play" these children and adults are able to become something they are not; something that cannot be. How much more powerful, then, must a mask be when the transformation is considered "real?"

Masking has been around for at least 20,000 years. Images painted on cave walls in southern France depict human bodies with animal heads. This evidence has led some scholars to conclude that the association of these masked figures to drawings of animals is an indication of masked rituals or shamanistic rites intended to insure the continued presence of game. Certainly, masking is closely associated with shamanistic performance in Asia, North America, and Africa, but archaeologists and art historians can only speculate about the purpose and meaning of these masked representations.

More conclusive evidence of a masking tradition is found at a site in the Sahara Desert dating to 10,000 years ago. The mask portrayed there bears a strong resemblance to masks used in West Africa in recent times. A masking tradition also existed in prehistoric Europe between 7,000 and 8,000 years ago.

Masks were made and used in the great civilizations of the Old and New Worlds. Death masks accompanied the Egyptian mummy to the tomb, and allowed the soul of the deceased to recognize its body after it returned to the tomb in the evening. Masks were used by the Aztecs and Maya of Middle America, and the Inca and other civilizations of the Andes. The Chinese, Indians, and Japanese used masks from ancient times in a variety of different ways including theater, as did the Greeks and Romans. Finally, tribal and fold societies continue to use masks ritually today.

The early Christian Church took a dim view of masking and suppressed it whenever possible. This was partly due to its association with pagan rites, and partly because of the "immoral" behavior that was often released through the anonymity afforded by the mask. However, the Church's efforts at suppression were not entirely successful. In rural Europe, masking customs survived as Carnival and Mardi Gras; with the rise of the *commedia dell'arte* during the Renaissance, and the subsequent emergence of secular theater, masking was once again firmly established in European tradition.

In tribal societies masks are agents for curing illness, for combating witchcraft and sorcery, and for correcting the causes of affliction in general. The False Faces of the Iroquois people have this function, as do certain kinds of masks used in West Africa. Shamans, already mentioned as likely candidates for the first masked performers, wear masks when they journey to the Spirit World. The mask image represents the shaman's spirit guide who protects him or her during the journey, and once in the spirit realm, aids in locating the cause of affliction so that it can be cured.

In other cultures the mask represents the forces of nature and life. Often these forces or energies are recorded in myths and are given human or animal form, as on the Northwest Coast of North America, and in some parts of Africa. Rituals performed for the continuance of life, so called "fertility rites," also often involved masked performance, and usually correspond to seasonal changes or planting and harvesting ceremonies. The Pueblo peoples of the Southwestern United States perform dances to promote fertility and rainfall, as do Africans living in the drier regions of the Western Sudan.

Dramatic performances and entertainment are important functions that masks perform, especially in more complex cultures. It is interesting to note that the Greek word for drama and the word for ritual, "enon," have a common root meaning "a thing done." Historically, Greek drama, which was and is a masked performance, began as a masked ritual. Over time the religious aspects of masked drama gave way to a more secular function of entertainment. In Indonesia, India, China, Japan and Europe, masked theater continues to be performed, either with religious or semi-religious overtones, while masked festivals are found throughout Europe, Central and South America and often coordinate with significant Church holidays.

One of the most important things that masks do is transform the identity of the wearer, and *changing* identity is not the same thing as transforming it. In New Guinea, West and Central Africa, and North America masks are used in "rites of passage." These rituals mark important transitions in the life cycle of individuals, or classes of individuals, in a society. Initiation into adulthood or a secret society, marriage, movement to a higher social rank, and funeral ceremonies are events that are often marked by masked performance. Death and rebirth are common themes in rites of passage, and are frequently given visual form in the mask. In a rite of passage, an earlier identity ceases to exist, and is symbolically replaced with a new and entirely different identity.

Our word "larva" can further illustrate the difference between change and transformation. English speakers recognize the term *larva* as referring to an immature stage in the developmental cycle of an animal, usually an insect. A caterpillar, for example, is the larval stage of a moth or butterfly. In Latin *larva* originally meant either a mask or a spirit or ghost. Thus, the caterpillar is a "mask" that the butterfly wears until it is transformed into a moth. The caterpillar does not simply change, it becomes something else, a totally different entity.

"Sowei" masks worn by the Bundu Society of the Mende and other West African tribes of Liberia and Sierra Leone, use the image of the chrysalis as a visible metaphor for the transformation of a girl into a woman through initiation. In this wonderful analogy, the larva/girl becomes a butterfly/woman through the transformative process of the chrysalis/initiation rite. After their rites of passage, the newly formed women publicly dance in their masks to announce that a transformation has indeed taken place, and that the girls that used to be no longer exist. Henceforth, they are expected to behave as women, and are treated as such.

An equally graphic example of this process is provided by certain masks made by the Indians of British Columbia. These "transformation" masks show the double nature of human beings —both an animal and "something-other-than-animal." The mask represents an animal spirit that stands in a special relationship to the masker or his family group. Recognition of this link between the human world and the spirit/animal world establishes an intimate connection between all forms of life. It presents in tangible form the belief of these Indians that animals and spirits are people "masks" and that humankind is directly and personally responsible for maintaining Cosmic Order. Humans accept this responsibility by transforming themselves into animals or spirits through the agency of the mask, and by performing the dances and rituals belonging to the mask spirit. Performances feed the spirits as the spirits feed humankind, and the mask becomes an icon for the interdependence of the forces which collectively comprise the Cosmos.

The Northwest Coast tribes, like many other peoples, believe that supernatural power resides in the mask itself. This power is released when a human puts on the mask and it is the spirit of the mask which performs, and not the "man-that-was." He has become something beyond the human, and through this metamorphosis the audience, too, is transformed. It is elevated from the routine duties of daily life, and transported into a different plane of reality where contradiction, conflict and ambiguity are resolved into a fundamental unity. In this "altered state," shared by both the masker and the audience, basic truths and values are rediscovered as personal desires are set aside in favor of a common good. The "self," the society, and the Universe are once again set in order through the powerful symbolism of the masked ritual dance. This feeling of "wholeness" is not limited to the experience of tribal people. We have all experienced it after viewing a powerful dramatic performance or motion picture. It is as though the "as if" quality, the pretense of the play, was somehow more "real" than the reality we take for granted. Our modern performers usually do not wear masks, but they are "personae" nonetheless.

Masks encourage us to transform ourselves, and empower us to do so. They permit us to replace one reality with another. They can ultimately provide us with a better understanding of who we really are behind the masks we put on every morning and take off every night in our dreams.

As a man strolls through a crowded marketplace, he comes upon a statue. It is the most incredibly lifelike statue he has ever seen. Luckily its creator is nearby and sees the man admiring his work. "So you like the statue," the creator says to the man. "Why yes, it's amazing. How can it be that there is not a man inside upon which an outer shell has been constructed?" he asks. "There is," the creator replies. The man is shocked. "What! How could you live with yourself making someone suffer so—merely for art?" The creator sighs, "Alas, it is myself inside the mask."

—A Parable

Aubrey Beardsley

Carnival

Gabriel Q

I put on my mask, adjust my gold lamé and see-through lace, put the door key in my shoe and step out into the morning fog. Suddenly everything has meaning.

It's Mardi Gras in New Orleans. My mask has taken me into a mythical landscape where I discover that I'm not alone. Dozens, then hundreds, then thousands of us are merging and twirling in an ancient ritual of joyful rebirth. The city has become ritual space made sacred by our masks and our imaginations. Even the fog has joined in, masking the modern skyline and leaving only the eyes of the 19th-century French doors and iron balconies full of more costumed deities watching the scene from behind their masks. Everybody's performing. Everybody's watching.

In a mask I look different. But more important, I am treated differently and so I experience a new being. Slowly, I become my vision. I become mythic. The mask allows me the privacy to fully experience this personal revelation without withdrawing. I look at the beauty and mystery all around me and I am in tears. The band is playing and the crowd is singing "Everyday Is Mardi Gras in Heaven." In lurid fits of ecstasy and excess, in sequins and leather and feathers and duct tape, these carnival revelers and I reinvent ancient rituals of renewal, heralding the coming of Spring.

Man is not merely the sum of his masks. Behind the shifting face of personality is a hard nugget of self, a genetic gift.... The self is malleable but elastic, snapping back to its original shape like a rubber band. Mental illness is no myth, as some have claimed. It is a disturbance in our sense of possession of a stable inner self that survives its personae.

—Camille Paglia
Sex, Art, and American Culture

Henry Jekyll's Full Statement of the Case

Robert Louis Stevenson

I was born in the year 18— to a large fortune, endowed besides with excellent parts, inclined by nature to industry, fond of the respect of the wise and good among my fellowmen, and thus, as might have been supposed, with every guarantee of an honourable and distinguished future. And indeed the worst of my faults was a certain impatient gaiety of disposition, such as has made the happiness of many, but such as I found it hard to reconcile with my imperious desire to carry my head high, and wear a more than commonly grave countenance before the public. Hence it came about that I concealed my pleasures; and that when I reached years of reflection, and began to look round me and take stock of my progress and position in the world, I stood already committed to a profound duplicity of me. Many a man would have even blazoned such irregularities as I was guilty of; but from the high views that I had set before me, I regarded and hid them with an almost morbid sense of shame. It was thus rather the exacting nature of my aspirations than any particular degradation in my faults, that made me what I was, and, with even a deeper trench than in the majority of men, severed in me those provinces of good and ill which divide and compound man's dual nature. In this case, I was driven to reflect deeply and inveterately on that hard law of life, which lies at the root of religion and is one of the most plentiful springs of distress. Though so profound a double-dealer,

I was in no sense a hypocrite; both sides of me were in dead earnest; I was no more myself when I laid aside restraint and plunged in shame, than when I laboured, in the eye of day, at the futherance of knowledge or the relief of sorrow and suffering. And it chanced that the direction of my scientific studies, which led wholly towards the mystic and the transcendental, reacted and shed a strong light on this consciousness of the perennial war among my members. With every day, and from both sides of my intelligence, the moral and the intellectual, I thus drew steadily nearer to that truth, by whose partial discovery I have been doomed to such a dreadful shipwreck: that man is not truly one, but truly two. I say two, because the state of my own knowledge does not pass beyond that point. Others will follow, others will outstrip me on the same lines; and I hazard the guess that man will be ultimately known for a mere polity of multifarious, incongruous and independent denizens. I, for my part, from the nature of my life, advanced infallibly in one direction and in one direction only. It was on the moral side, and in my own person, that I learned to recognise the thorough and primitive duality of man; I saw that, of the two natures that contended in the field of my consciousness, even if I could rightly be said to be either, it was only because I was radically both; and from an early date, even before the course of my scientific discoveries had begun to suggest the most naked possibility of such a miracle, I had learned to dwell with pleasure, as a beloved daydream, on the thought of the separation of these elements. If each, I told myself, could be housed in separate identities, life would be relieved of all that was unbearable; the unjust might go his way, delivered from the aspirations and remorse of his more upright twin; and the just could walk steadfastly and securely on his upward path, doing the good things in which he found his pleasure, and no longer exposed to disgrace and penitence by the hands of this extraneous evil. It was the curse of mankind that these incongruous faggots were thus bound together—that in the agonised womb of consciousness, these polar

46

twins should be continuously struggling. How, then were they dissociated?

I was so far in my reflections when, as I have said, a side light began to shine upon the subject from the laboratory table. I began to perceive more deeply than it has ever yet been stated, the trembling immateriality, the mistlike transience, of this seemingly so solid body in which we walk attired. Certain agents I found to have the power to shake and pluck back that fleshly vestment, even as a wind might toss the curtains of a pavilion. For two good reasons, I will not enter deeply into this scientific branch of my confession. First, because I have been made to learn that the doom and burthen of our life is bound for ever on man's shoulders, and when the attempt is made to cast it off, it but returns upon us with more unfamiliar and more awful pressure. Second, because, as my narrative will make, alas! too evident, my discoveries were incomplete. Enough then, that I not only recognised my natural body from the mere aura and effulgence of certain of the powers that made up my spirit, but managed to compound a drug by which these powers should be dethroned from their supremacy, and a second form and countenance substituted, none the less natural to me because they were the expression, and bore the stamp of lower elements in my soul.

I hesitated long before I put this theory to the test of practice. I knew well that I risked death; for any drug that so potently controlled and shook the very fortress of identity, might, by the least scruple of an overdose or at the least inopportunity in the moment of exhibition, utterly blot out that immaterial tabernacle which I looked to it to change. But the temptation of a discovery so singular and profound at last overcame the suggestions of alarm. I had long since prepared my tincture; I purchased at once, from a firm of wholesale chemists, a large quantity of a particular salt which I knew, from my experiments, to be the last ingredient required; and late one accursed night, I compounded the elements, watched them boil and smoke together in the glass, and when the ebullition had subsided, with a strong glow of courage, drank off the potion.

The most racking pangs succeeded: a grinding in the bones, deadly nausea, and a horror of the spirit that cannot be exceeded at the hour of birth or death. Then these agonies began swiftly to subside, and I came to myself as if out of a great sickness. There was something strange in my sensations, something indescribably new and, from its very novelty, incredibly sweet. I felt younger, lighter, happier in body; within I was conscious of a heady recklessness, a current of disordered sensual images running like a millrace in my fancy, a solution of the bonds of obligation, an unknown but not an innocent freedom of the soul. I knew myself, at the first breath of this new life, to be more wicked, tenfold more wicked, sold a slave to my original evil; and the thought, in that moment, braced and delighted me like wine. I stretched out my hands, exulting in the freshness of these sensations; and in the act, I was suddenly aware that I had lost in stature.

There was no mirror, at that date, in my room; that which stands beside me as I write, was brought there later on and for the very purpose of these transformations. The night however, was far gone into the morning—the morning, black as it was, was nearly ripe for the conception of the day—the inmates of my house were locked in the most rigorous hours of slumber; and I determined, flushed as I was with hope and triumph, to venture in my new shape as far as to my bedroom. I crossed the yard, wherein the constellations looked down upon me, I could have thought, with wonder, the first creature of that sort that their unsleeping vigilance had yet disclosed to them; I stole through the corridors, a stranger in my own house; and coming to my room, I saw for the first time the appearance of Edward Hyde.

I must here speak by theory alone, saying not that which I know, but that which I suppose to be most probable. The evil side of my nature, to which I had now transferred the stamping efficacy, was less robust and less developed than the good which I had just deposed. Again, in the course of my life, which had been, after all, nine tenths a life of effort, virtue and control, it had been much less exercised and much less exhausted. And hence, as I think, it came about that Edward Hyde was so much smaller, slighter and younger than Henry Jekyll. Even as good shone upon the countenance of the one, evil was written broadly and plainly on the face of the other. Evil besides (which I must still believe to be the lethal side of man) had left on that body an imprint of deformity and decay. And yet when I looked upon that ugly idol in the glass, I was conscious of no repugnance, rather of a leap of welcome. This, too, was myself. It seemed natural and human. In my eyes it bore a livelier image of the spirit, it seemed more express and single, than the imperfect and divided countenance I had been hitherto accustomed to call mine. And in so far I was doubtless right. I have observed that when I wore the semblance of Edward Hyde, none could come near to me at first without a visible misgiving of the flesh. This, as I take it, was because all human beings, as we meet them, are commingled out of good and evil: and Edward Hyde, alone in the ranks of mankind, was pure evil.

I lingered but a moment at the mirror: the second and conclusive experiment had yet to be attempted; it yet remained to be seen if I had lost my identity beyond redemption and must flee before daylight from a house that was no longer mine; and hurrying back to my cabinet, I once more prepared and drank the cup, once more suffered the pangs of dissolution, and came to myself once more with the character, the stature and the face of Henry Jekyll.

That night I had come to the fatal cross-roads. Had I approached my discovery in a more noble spirit, had I risked the experiment while under the empire of generous or pious aspirations, all must have been otherwise, and from these agonies of death and birth, I had come forth an angel instead of a fiend. The drug had no discriminating action; it was neither diabolical nor divine; it but shook the doors of the prisonhouse of my disposition; and like the captives of Philippi, that which stood within ran forth. At that time my virtue slumbered; my evil, kept awake by ambition, was alert and swift to seize the occasion; and the thing that was projected was Edward Hyde. Hence, although I had now two characters as well as two appearances, one was wholly evil, and the other was still the old Henry Jekyll, that incongruous compound of whose reformation and improvement I had already learned to despair. The movement was thus wholly toward the worse.

Even at that time, I had not conquered my aversions to the dryness of a life of study. I would still be merrily disposed at times; and as my pleasures were (to say the least) undignified, and I was not only well known and highly considered, but growing towards the elderly man, this incoherency of my life was daily growing more unwelcome. It was on this side that my new power tempted me until I fell in slavery. I had but to drink the cup, to doff at once the body of the noted professor, and to assume, like a thick cloak, that of Edward Hyde. I smiled at the notion; it seemed to me at the time to be humourous; and I made my preparations with the most studious care. I took and furnished that house in Soho, to which Hyde was tracked by the police; and engaged as a housekeeper a creature whom I knew well to be silent and unscrupulous. On the other side, I announced to my servants that a Mr. Hyde (whom I described) was to have full liberty and power about my house in the square; and to parry mishaps, I even called and made myself a familiar object, in my second character. I next drew up that will to which you so much objected; so that if anything befell me in the person of Dr. Jekyll, I could enter on that of Edward Hyde without pecuniary loss. And thus fortified, as I supposed, on every side, I began to profit by the strange immunities of my position.

Men have before hired bravos to transact their crimes, while their own person and reputation sat under shelter. I was the first that ever did so for his pleasures. I was the first that could plod in the public eye with a load of genial respectability, and in a moment, like a schoolboy, strip off these lendings and spring headlong into the sea of liberty. But for me, in my impenetrable mantle, the safely was complete. Think of it—I did not even exist! Let me but escape into my laboratory door, give me but a second or two to mix and swallow the draught that I had always standing ready; and whatever he had done, Edward Hyde would pass away like the stain of breath upon a mirror; and there in his stead, quietly at home, trimming the midnight lamp in his study, a man who could afford to laugh at suspicion, would be Henry Jekyll.

The pleasures which I made haste to seek in my disguise were, as I have said, undignified; I would scarce use a harder term. But in the hands of Edward Hyde, they soon began to turn toward the monstrous. When I would come back from these excursions, I was often plunged into a kind of wonder at my vicarious depravity. This familiar that I called out of my own soul, and sent forth alone to do his good pleasure, was a being inherently malign and villainous; his every act and thought centered on self; drinking pleasure with bestial avidity from any degree of torture to another; relentless like a man of stone. Henry Jekyll stood at times aghast before the acts of Edward Hyde; but the situation was apart from ordinary laws, and insidiously relaxed the grasp of conscience. It was Hyde, after all, and Hyde alone, that was guilty. Jekyll was no worse; he woke again to his good qualities seemingly unimpaired; he would even make haste, where it was possible, to undo the evil done by Hyde. And thus his conscience slumbered.

Into the details of the infamy at which I thus connived (for even now I can scarce grant that I committed it) I have no design of entering; I mean but to point out the warnings and the successive steps with which my chastisement approached. I met with one accident which, as it brought on no consequence, I shall no more than mention. An act of cruelty to a child aroused against me the anger of a passer-by, whom I recognised the other day in the person of your kinsman; the doctor and the child's family joined him; there were moments when I feared for my life; and at last, in order to pacify their too just resentment, Edward Hyde had to bring them to the door, and pay them in a cheque drawn in the name of Henry Jekyll. But this danger was easily eliminated from the future, by opening an account at another bank in the name of Edward Hyde himself; and when, by sloping my own hand backward, I had supplied my double with a signature, I thought I sat beyond the reach of fate.

Some two months before the murder of Sir Danvers, I had been out for one of my adventures, had returned at a late hour, and woke the next day in bed with somewhat odd sensations. It was in vain I looked about me; in vain I saw the decent furniture and tall proportions of my room in the square; in vain that I recognised the pattern of the bed curtains and the design of the mahogany frame; something still kept insisting that I was not where I was, that I had not wakened where I seemed to be, but in the little room in Soho where I was accustomed to sleep in the body of Edward Hyde. I smiled to myself, and in my psychological way, began lazily to inquire into the elements of this illusion, occasionally, even as I did so, dropping back into a comfortable morning doze. I was still so engaged when, in one of my more wakeful moments, my eyes fell upon my hand. Now the hand of Henry Jekyll (as you have often remarked) was professional in shape and size: it was large, firm, white and comely. But the hand which I now saw, clearly enough, in the yellow light of a mid-London morning, lying half shut on the bedclothes, was lean, corder, knuckly, of a dusky pallor and thickly shaded with a swart growth of hair. It was the hand of Edward Hyde.

I must have stared upon it for near half a minute, sunk as I was in the mere stupidity of wonder, before terror woke up in my breast as sudden and startling as the crash of cymbals; and bounding from my bed I rushed to the mirror. At the sight that met my eyes, my blood was changed into something exquisitely thin and icy. Yes, I had gone to bed Henry Jekyll, I had awakened Edward Hyde. How was this to be explained? I asked myself; and then, with another bound of terror—how was it to be remedied? It was well on in the morning; the servants were up; all my drugs were in the cabinet—a long journey down two pairs of stairs, through the back passage, across the open court and through the anatomical theatre, from where I was then standing horror-struck. It might indeed be possible to cover my face; but of what use was that, when I was unable to conceal the alteration in my stature? And then with an overpowering sweetness of relief, it came back upon my mind that the servants were already used to the coming and going of my second self. I had soon dressed, as well as I was able, in clothes of my own size: had soon passed through the house, where Bradshaw stared and drew back at seeing Mr. Hyde at such an hour and in such a strange array; and ten minutes later, Dr. Jekyll had returned to his own shape and was sitting down, with a darkened brow, to make a feint of breakfasting.

Small indeed was my appetite. This inexplicable incident, this reversal of my previous experience, seemed, like the Babylonian finger on the wall, to be spelling out the letters of my judgment; and I began to reflect more seriously than ever before on the issues and possibilities of my double existence. That part of me which I had the power of projecting, had lately been much exercised and nourished; it had seemed to me of late as though the body of Edward Hyde had grown in stature, as though (when I wore that form) I were conscious of a more generous tide of blood; and I began to spy a danger that, if this were much prolonged, the balance of my nature might be permanently overthrown, the power of voluntary change be forfeited, and the character of Edward Hyde become irrevocably mine. The power of the drug had not been always equally displayed. Once, very early in my career, it had totally failed me; since then I had been obliged on more than one occasion to double, and once, with infinite risk of death, to treble the amount; and these rare uncertainties had cast hitherto the sole shadow on my contentment. Now, however, and in the light of that morning's accident, I was led to remark that whereas, in the beginning, the difficulty had been to throw off the body of Jekyll, it had of late gradually but decidedly transferred itself to the other side. All things therefore seemed to point to this; that I was slowly losing hold of my original and better self, and becoming slowly incorporated with my second and worse.

Between these two, I now felt I had to choose. My two natures had memory in common, but all other faculties were most unequally shared between them. Jekyll (who was composite) now with the most sensitive apprehensions, now with a greedy gusto, projected and shared in the pleasures and adventures of Hyde; but Hyde was indifferent to Jekyll, or but remembered him as the mountain bandit remembers the cavern in which he conceals himself from pursuit. Jekyll had more than a father's interest; Hyde had more than a son's indifference. To cast in my lot with Jekyll, was to die to those appetites which I had long secretly indulged and had of late begun to pamper. To cast it in with Hyde, was to die to a thousand interests and aspirations, and to become, at a blow and forever, despised and friendless. The bargain might appear unequal; but there was still another consideration in the scales; for while Jekyll would suffer smartingly in the fires of abstinence, Hyde would be not even conscious of all that he had lost. Strange as my circumstances were, the terms of this debate are as old and commonplace as man; much the same inducements and alarms cast the die for any tempted and trembling sinner; and it fell out with me, as it falls with so vast a majority of my fellows, that I chose the better part and was found wanting in the strength to keep to it.

Yes, I preferred the elderly and discontented doctor, surrounded by friends and cherishing honest hopes; and bade a resolute farewell to the liberty, the comparative youth, the light step, leaping impulses and secret pleasures, that I had enjoyed in the disguise of Hyde. I made this choice perhaps with some unconscious reservation, for I neither gave up the house in Soho, nor destroyed the clothes of Edward Hyde, which still lay ready in my cabinet. For two months, however, I was true to my determination; for two months, I led a life of such severity as I had never before attained to, and enjoyed the compensations of an approving conscience. But time began at last to obliterate the freshness of my alarm; the praises of conscience began to grow into a thing of course; I began to be tortured with throes and longings, as of Hyde struggling after freedom; and at last, in an hour of moral weakness, I once again compounded and swallowed the transforming draught.

I do not suppose that, when a drunkard reasons with himself upon his vice, he is once out of five hundred times affected by the dangers that he runs through his brutish, physical insensibility; neither had I, long as I had considered my position, made enough allowance for the complete moral insensibility and insensate readiness to evil, which were the leading characters of Edward Hyde. Yet it was by these that I was punished. My devil had been long caged, he came out roaring. I was conscious, even when I took the draught, of a more unbridled, a more furious propensity to ill. It must have been this, I suppose, that stirred in my soul that tempest of impatience with which I listened to the civilities of my unhappy victim; I declare, at least, before God, no man morally sane could have been guilty of that crime upon so pitiful a provocation; and that I struck in no more reasonable spirit than that in which a sick child may break a plaything. But I had voluntarily stripped myself of all those balancing instincts by which even the worst of us continues to walk with some degree of steadiness among temptations; and in my case, to be tempted, however slightly, was to fall.

Instantly the spirit of hell awoke in me and raged. With a transport of glee, I mauled the unresisting body, tasting delight from every blow; and it was not till weariness had begun to succeed, that I was suddenly, in the top fit of my delirium, struck through the heart by a cold thrill of terror. A mist dispersed; I saw my life to be forfeit; and fled from the scene of these excesses, at once glorying and trembling, my lust of evil gratified and stimulated, my love of life screwed to the topmost peg. I ran to the house in Soho, and (to make assurance doubly sure) destroyed my papers; thence I set out through the lamplit streets, in the same divided ecstasy of mind, gloating on my crime, light-headedly devising others in the future, and yet still hastening and still hearkening in my wake for the steps of the avenger. Hyde had a song upon his lips as he compounded the draught, and as he drank it, pledged the dead man. The pangs of transformation had not done tearing him, before Henry Jekyll, with streaming tears of gratitude and remorse, had fallen upon his knees and lifted his clasped hands to God. The veil of self-indulgence was rent from head to foot. I saw my life as a whole: I followed it up from the days of childhood, when I had walked with my father's hand, and through the self-denying toils of my professional life, to arrive again and again, with the same sense of unreality, at the damned horrors of the evening. I could have screamed aloud; I sought with tears and prayers to smother down the crowd of hideous images and sounds with which my memory swarmed against me; and still, between the petitions, the ugly face of my iniquity stared into my soul. As the acuteness of this remorse began to die away, it was succeeded by a sense of joy. The problem of my conduct was solved. Hyde was thenceforth impossible; whether I would or not, I was now confined to the better part of my existence; and O, how I rejoiced to think of it! with what willing humility I embraced anew the restrictions of natural life! with what sincere renunciation I locked the door by which I had so often gone and come, and ground the key under my heel!

The next day, came the news that the murder had been overlooked, that the guilt of Hyde was patent to the world, and that the victim was a man high in public estimation. It was not only a crime, it had been a tragic folly. I think I was glad to know it; I think I was glad to have my better impulses thus buttressed and guarded by the terrors of the scaffold. Jekyll was now my city of refuge; let but Hyde peep out an instant, and the hands of all men would be raised to take and slay him.

I resolved in my future conduct to redeem the past; and I can say with honesty that my resolve was fruitful of some good. You know yourself how earnestly, in the last months of the last year, I laboured to relieve suffering; you know that much was done for others, and that the days passed quietly, almost happily for myself. Nor can I truly say that I wearied of this beneficent and innocent life; I think instead that I daily enjoyed it more completely; but I was still cursed with my duality of purpose; and as the first edge of my penitence wore off, the lower side of me, so long indulged, so recently chained down, began to growl for licence. Not that I dreamed of resuscitating Hyde; the bare idea of that would startle me to frenzy: no, it was in my own person that I was once more tempted to trifle with my conscience; and it was as an ordinary secret sinner that I at last fell before the assaults of temptation.

There comes an end to all things; the most capacious measure is filled at last; and this brief condescension to my evil finally destroyed the balance of my soul. And yet I was not alarmed; the fall seemed natural, like a return to the old days before I had made my discovery. It was a fine, clear, January day, wet under foot where the frost had melted, but cloudless overhead; and the Regent's Park was full of winter chirrupings and sweet with spring odours. I sat in the sun on a bench; the animal within me licking the chops of memory; the spiritual side a little drowsed, promising subsequent penitence, but not yet moved to begin. After all, I reflected, I was like my neighbours; and then I smiled, comparing myself with other men, comparing my active good-will with the lazy cruelty of their neglect. And at the very moment of that vainglorious thought, a qualm came over me, a horrid nausea and the most deadly shuddering. These passed away, and left me faint; and then as in its turn faintness subsided, I began to be aware of a change in the temper of my thoughts, a greater boldness, a contempt of danger, a solution of the bonds of obligation. I looked down; my clothes hung formlessly on my shrunken limbs; the hand that lay on my knee was corded and hairy. I was once more Edward Hyde. A moment before I had been safe of all men's respect, wealthy, beloved—the cloth laying for me in the dining-room at home; and now I was the common quarry of mankind, hunted, houseless, a known murderer, thrall to the gallows.

My reason wavered, but it did not fail me utterly. I have more than once observed that in my second character, my faculties seemed sharpened to a point and my spirits more tensely elastic; thus it came about that, where Jekyll perhaps might have succumbed, Hyde rose to the importance of the moment. My drugs were in one of the presses of my cabinet; how was I to reach them? That was the problem that (crushing my temples in my hands) I set myself to solve. The laboratory door I had closed. If I sought to enter by the house, my own servants would consign me to the gallows. I saw I must employ another hand, and thought of Lanyon. How was he to be reached? how persuaded? Supposing that I escaped capture in the streets, how was I to make my way into his presence? and how should I, an unknown and displeasing visitor, prevail on the famous physician to rifle the study of his colleague, Dr. Jekyll? Then I remembered that of my original character, one part remained to me: I could write my own hand; and once I had conceived that kindling spark, the way that I must follow became lighted up from end to end.

Thereupon, I arranged my clothes as best I could, and summoning a passing hansom, drove to an hotel in Portland Street, the name of which I chanced to remember. At my appearance (which was indeed comical enough, however tragic a fate these garments covered) the driver could not conceal his mirth. I gnashed my teeth upon him with a gust of devilish fury; and the smile withered from his face—happily for him—yet more happily for myself, for in another instant I had certainly dragged him from his perch. At the inn, as I entered, I looked about me with so black a countenance as made the attendants tremble; not a look did they exchange in my presence; but obsequiously took my orders, led me to a private room, and brought me wherewithal to write. Hyde in danger of his life was a creature new to me; shaken with inordinate anger, strung to the pitch of murder, lusting to inflict pain. Yet the creature was astute; mastered his fury with a great effort of the will; composed his two important letters, one to Lanyon and one to Poole; and that he might receive actual evidence of their being posted, sent them out with directions that they should be registered. Thenceforward, he sat all day over the fire in the private room, gnawing his nails; there he dined, sitting alone with his fears, the waiter visibly quailing before his eye; and thence, when the night was fully come, he set forth in the corner of a closed cab, and was driven to and fro about the streets of the city. He, I say—I cannot say, I. That child of Hell had nothing human; nothing lived in him but fear and hatred. And when at last, thinking the driver had begun to grow suspicious, he discharged the cab and ventured on foot, attired in his misfitting clothes, an object marked out for observation, into the midst of the nocturnal passengers, these two base passions raged within him like a tempest. He walked fast, hunted by his fears, chattering to himself, skulking through the less frequented thoroughfares, counting the minutes that still divided him from midnight. Once a woman spoke to him, offering, I think, a box of lights. He smote her in the face, and she fled.

When I came to myself at Lanyon's, the horror of my old friend perhaps affected me somewhat: I do not know; it was at least but a drop in the sea to the abhorrence with which I looked back upon these hours. A change had come over me. It was no longer the fear of the gallows, it was the horror of being Hyde that racked me. I received Lanyon's condemnation partly in a dream; it was partly in a dream that I came home to my own house and got into bed. I slept after the prostration of the day, with a stringent and profound slumber which not even the nightmares that wrung me could avail to break. I awoke in the morning shaken, weakened, but refreshed. I still hated and feared the thought of the brute that slept within me, and I had not of course forgotten the appalling dangers of the day before; but I was once more at home, in my own house and close to my drugs; and gratitude for my escape shone so strong in my soul that it almost rivalled the brightness of hope.

I was stepping leisurely across the court after breakfast, drinking the chill of the air with pleasure, when I was seized again with those indescribable sensations that heralded the change; and I had but the time to gain the shelter of my cabinet, before I was once again raging and freezing with the passions of Hyde. It took on this occasion a double dose to recall me to myself; and alas! six hours after, as I sat looking sadly in the fire, the pangs returned, and the drug had to be re-administered. In short, from that day forth it seemed only by a great effort as of gymnastics, and only under the immediate stimulation of the drug, that I was able to wear the countenance of Jekyll. At all hours of the day and night, I would be taken with the premonitory shudder; above all, if I slept, or even dozed for a moment in my chair, it was always as Hyde that I awakened. Under the strain of this continually impending doom and by the sleeplessness to which I now condemned myself, ay, even beyond what I had thought possible to man, I became, in my own person, a creature eaten up and emptied by fever, languidly weak both in body and mind, and solely occupied by one thought: the horror of my other self. But when I slept, or when the virtue of the medicine wore off, I would leap almost without transition (for the pangs of transformation grew daily less marked) into the possession of a fancy brimming with images of terror, a soul boiling with causeless hatreds, and a body that seemed not strong enough to contain the raging energies of life. The powers of Hyde seemed to have grown with the sickliness of Jekyll. And certainly the hate that now divided them was equal on each side. With Jekyll, it was a thing of vital instinct. He had now seen the full deformity of that creature that shared with him some of the phenomena of consciousness, and was co-heir with him to death: and beyond these links of community, which in themselves made the most poignant part of his distress, he thought of Hyde, for all his energy of life, as of something not only hellish but inorganic. This was the shocking thing; that the slime of the pit seemed to utter cries and voices; that the amorphous dust gesticulated and sinned; that what was dead, and had no shape, should usurp the offices of life. And this again, that that insurgent horror was knit to him closer than a wife, closer than an eye; lay caged in his flesh, where he heard it mutter and felt it struggle to be born; and at every hour of weakness, and in the confidence of slumber, prevailed against him, and deposed him out of life. The hatred of Hyde for Jekyll was of a different order. His terror of the gallows drove him continually to commit temporary suicide, and return to his subordinate station of a part instead of a person; but he loathed the necessity, he loathed the despondency into which Jekyll was now fallen, and he resented the dislike with which he was himself regarded. Hence the ape-like tricks that he would play me, scrawling in my own hand blasphemies on the pages of my books, burning the letters and destroying the portrait of my father; and indeed, had it not been for his fear of death, he would long ago have ruined himself in order to involve me in the ruin. But his love of me is wonderful; I go further: I, who sicken and freeze at the mere thought of him, when I recall the abjection and passion of this attachment, and when I know how he fears my power to cut him off by suicide, I find it in my heart to pity him.

It is useless, and the time awfully fails me, to prolong this description; no one has ever suffered such torments, let that suffice; and yet even to these, habit brought—no, not alleviation— but a certain callousness of soul, a certain acquiescence of despair; and my punishment might have gone on for years, but for the last calamity which has now fallen, and which has finally severed me from my own face and nature. My provision of the salt, which had never been renewed since the date of the first experiment, began to run low. I sent out for a fresh supply and mixed the draught; the ebullition followed, and the first change of colour, not the second; I drank it and it was without efficiency. You will learn from Poole how I have had London ransacked; it was in vain; and I am now persuaded that my first supply was impure, and that it was that unknown impurity which lent efficacy to the draught.

About a week has passed, and I am now finishing this statement under the influence of the last of the old powders. This, then, is the last time, short of a miracle, that Henry Jekyll can think his own thoughts or see his own face (now how sadly altered!) in the glass. Nor must I delay too long to bring my writing to an end; for if my narrative has hitherto escaped destruction, it has been by a combination of great prudence and great good luck. Should the throes of change take me in the act of writing it, Hyde will tear it in pieces; but if some time shall have elapsed after I have laid it by, his wonderful selfishness and circumscription to the moment will probably save it once again from the action of his ape-like spite. And indeed the doom that is closing on us both has already changed and crushed him. Half an hour from now, when I shall again and forever reindue that hated personality, I know how I shall sit shuddering and weeping in my chair, or continue, with the most strained and fearstruck ecstasy of listening, to pace up and down this room (my last earthly refuge) and give ear to every sound of menace. Will Hyde die upon the scaffold? or will he find courage to release himself at the last moment? God knows; I am careless; this is my true hour of death, and what is to follow concerns another than myself. Here then, as I lay down the pen and proceed to seal up my confession, I bring the life of that unhappy Henry Jekyll to an end.

A Fox entered the house of an actor and, rummaging through all his properties, came upon a Mask, an admirable imitation of a human head. He placed his paws on it and said, "What a beautiful head! Yet it is of no value, as it entirely lacks brains."

—Aesop's Fables

By the Creek

Barry Yourgrau

I come into the kitchen. My mother screams. Finally she lowers her arm from in front of her face. "What are you doing, are you out of your *mind!*" she demands. I grin at her, in my bermudas and bare feet. "It's okay," I tell her in a chambered voice through my father's heavy, muffling lips. "He's taking a nap, he won't care." "What do you mean he won't *care*," she says. "It's his *head*. For god's sake put it back right now before he wakes up." "No," I tell her, pouting, disappointed that her only response is this remonstration. "I'll put it back in a while." "Not in a while, *now*," she says. She moves her hands as if to take the head from me, but then her hands stammer and withdraw, repulsed by horror. "My *god*," she says, grimacing, wide-eyed. She presses her hands to her face. "Go away! Go away from here!" "Mom," I protest, nonplussed. But she shrinks away from me. "Get out of here," she cries.

I stalk out of the kitchen. Hurt and surprised I plod heavily up the stairs. I go into my parents' bedroom. I stand at the foot of the bed. My father lies on his back, mercifully unable to snore, one arm slung across his drum-like hairy chest in a pose particular to his sleep. I look at him. Then I back away, stealthily, one step at a time, out the door. On silent, bare feet I steal frenetically down the hall, down the front stairs and out the front door. On the street I break into a run but the head sways violently and I slow to a scurrying walk, until I'm in the woods. Then I take my time on the path, brooding, my hands in my bermuda pockets. I come to the creek and stand balancing on dusty feet on a hot, prominent rock. The midafternoon sun lays heavy, glossy patches on the water and fills the trees with a still, hot, silent glare. A bumble bee drones past, then comes back and hovers inquiringly. I get off the rock and stoop down, bracing the head with one hand, and pick up a pebble. I get back on the rock and fling the pebble at the creek. It makes a ring in the water. Another ring suddenly blooms beside it. I look around at the path. A friend of mind comes out of the trees. "Hi," I say to him. "Hi," he says, in a muffled, confined voice. He stops a few feet from me. "You look funny," he says. "So do you," I tell him. I make room for him on the rock. "Where's your dad?" I ask him. "In the hammock," he says. "Where's yours?" "We don't have a hammock," I tell him. "He's in bed."

Half an hour later there are half a dozen of us standing great-headed at the side of the creek.

Every philosophy also *conceals* a philosophy; every opinion is also a hideout, every word a mask.

—Friedrich Nietzsche
Beyond Good & Evil

Contributors

Samuel Avital is an artist, performer, teacher, mentor, creative consultant, and author. He taught mime for over 40 years, and is known as a talented, magnetic and inspiring teacher. Avital studied mime and theatre in Paris with Decroux and Marceau, and toured Europe before coming to the USA in the mid-1960s. He founded *Le Centre du Silence* Mime School in Boulder, Colorado in 1971 and facilitates the International Summer Mime Workspace yearly. He also offers private coaching to individuals and groups in the USA and abroad. Avital developed a method of teaching called *BodySpeak™ the Whole Being Training*. For the workbook, his other publications, or information about program training, write, call, email or visit LCDS Web site. *Le Centre du Silence* Mime School, Samuel Avital, Director, PO Box 1015, Boulder, CO 80306-1015, (303) 661-9271.

Born and raised in New York City, **Flint Butera** has been a part of the New York art scene for the past thirteen years. His provocative work has appeared on the Sci-Fi Channel and at a number of art venues in and around NYC. He recently had his first solo gallery opening in Chicago. His art has found its way into collections on every continent. A documentary film about his life and work by New York filmmaker Drew Naprawa will debut in 2004. See www.artphobia.com.

Wendy Klein is a maskmaker and sculptor living in Woodstock, New York. Her mask work can be seen at www.wendyklein.com.

Vincent Lloyd received his bachelor's degree from Princeton University in 2003 where he majored in religion. He is currently a graduate student in the rhetoric department at the University of California–Berkeley. From 1999-2003 he was Publisher of *CommonSense: The Intercollegiate Journal of Humanism and Freethought* and has been active in various political groups supporting low-wage workers and advocating for Palestinian rights.

Michael Perkins is the author of five collections of poetry, including the *Blue Woman* (1966), *The Persistence of Desire* (1977), *Praise in the Ears of Clouds* (1982), *Gift of Choice* (1992), and *I Could Walk All Day* (2002). *The Secret Record*, literary criticism, was published by William Morrow in 1976. Among his other works of fiction and non-fiction are the novels *Evil Companions* (1968, 1992, 2003), and *Dark Matter* (1996, 2002).

Gabriel Q is a maskmaker, puppeteer and performer living in Vermont. He draws inspiration from the New Orleans Mardi Gras while his technique is from the tradition of Italian paper maché. As a performer, he specializes in altering the human body to merge puppets with live actors. He is best known for his performance, "The Garden Variety Show" where the puppets are plants and animals in a metaphorical garden. Standing on long-legged roots, Gabriel plays the garden. See www.gabrielq.com.

Brent Robison is a writer, editor, and photographer living in Woodstock, New York. See www.brentrobison.com.

Sophie Rogers-Gessert, currently finishing a degree in linguistic anthropology at Sarah Lawrence College, is a poet, philosopher, artist, maker of new words, and private tutor. She is a contributing researcher for an upcoming book on the concept of "transgender" published by Duke University Press. She is also currently at work on a cross-cultural study of love, and spends her free time defending her title as the East Coast's original grammatically-improved linguistically-oriented pseudo positive logicalist.

Mark Sherman is a writer, songwriter, and retired professor of psychology at SUNY, New Paltz, New York. He has a long-standing interest in gender issues, which has been a main focus of his teaching, research, and writing for many years. He is currently at work on a project in this field. Sherman lives in New Paltz and writes a bi-weekly column for the *New Paltz Times*.

Sparrow lives in Phoenicia, New York, with his wife (Violet Snow), his daughter (Sylvia) and an off-white rabbit (Bananacake). His column "Heard By A Bird" in the *Phoenicia Times*, where he recounts local gossip, has earned him the sobriquet "the rural Liz Smith." Sparrow works as a substitute hall monitor at Onteora High School and studies Taoism.

Robert Louis Stevenson, born in 1850, was a Scottish novelist, poet, and essayist who is most famous for *Treasure Island, Kidnapped,* and *The Strange Case of Dr. Jekyll and Mr. Hyde.* He was an avid traveler and prolific writer despite his lifelong struggle with tuberculosis. He died in Samoa in 1894. From Stevenson's *A Child's Garden of Verses*: "The world is so full of a number of things, I'm sure we should all be as happy as kings."

George Ulrich is a graduate of the University of Oklahoma and the University of Wisconsin-Milwaukee, and has been curator of African and Pacific Ethnology at the Milwaukee Public Museum since 1981. Additionally, he teaches courses in Anthropology and Art History for the University of Wisconsin-Milwaukee and the Milwaukee Institute of Art and Design. Ulrich has traveled, studied, and collected in West Africa, Australia, Papua New Guinea, Alaska, British Columbia, and Mexico. His current research interests include the representational traditions of the Mambila people of the Nigeria-Cameroons border, and the material culture of shamanism and other traditional healing systems.

Barry Yourgrau is the author of four books of short fiction, most recently, *Haunted Traveller* (Arcade). A performer as well as writer, he starred in the film version of his book, *The Sadness of Sex.* His first two collections, *A Man Jumps Out of An Airplane* and *Wearing Dad's Head,* are considered classics of the sudden-fiction genre. Upcoming are books for children: a fantasy novel, *My Curious Uncle Dudley*; and *Nasty Stories (for Nasty Boys and Girls).* His Web site is www.yourgrau.com.